£1.50

THE WORLD OF THE MAGIC ROUNDABOUT

THE MOVIE

B⊞XTREE

First published 2004 by Boxtree
an imprint of Pan Macmillan Ltd
Pan Macmillan, 20 New Wharf Road, London N1 9RR
Basingstoke and Oxford
Associated companies throughout the world
www.panmacmillan.com

ISBN 0 7522 25200

Produced under license by Pathé Pictures Limited

Pathé Pictures presents in association with
the UK Film Council and Pathé Renn, Pricel, France 2 Cinema and Canal +
a Films Action / SPZ Entertainment/ bolexbrothers Production
THE MAGIC ROUNDABOUT
Tom Baker Jim Broadbent Joanna Lumley Ian McKellen Kylie Minogue Bill Nighy
Robbie Williams Ray Winstone
Associate Producers Claude Gorsky Linda Marks Bruce Higham Andy Leighton
Vertigo Productions
Based upon original characters created by Serge Danot
with the participation of Martine Danot
Co-Writers Raoff Sanoussi Stéphane Sanoussi
Screenplay by Paul Bassett Davies with additional material by Tad Safran
Executive Producers Francois Ivernel Cameron McCracken Jill Sinclair Jake Eberts
Producers Laurent Rodon Pascal Rodon
Directed By Jean Duval Frank Passingham Dave Borthwick
© Pathé Fund Limited 2005.

1 3 5 7 9 8 6 4 2

A CIP catalogue record for this book is available from
the British Library.

Design by Dan Newman/Perfect Bound Ltd

Printed by CPI Bath

THE WORLD OF

THE

OF

THE MAGIC ROUNDABOUT™

ROUNDABOUT

THE MOVIE

Andy Lane & Paul Simpson

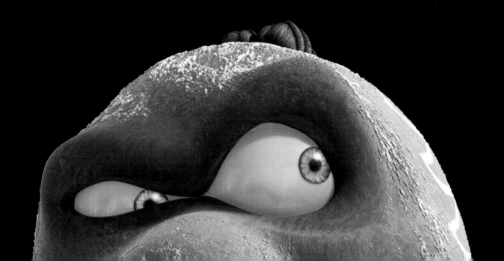

Contents

The Amazing Magic Roundabout

At the centre of the Enchanted Land lies the Enchanted Village. At the centre of the Enchanted Village is The Magic Roundabout. And that means The Magic Roundabout is at the centre of everything in the Enchanted Land.

It also means that when Dougal is on The Magic Roundabout everything revolves around him, which is what he has always believed anyway.

The Magic Roundabout is a place of fun and of friendship. It's a place where everyone can gather to talk, to play, to think quietly or just to sit on a wooden horse and twirl sedately round and round. It's a place where nobody worries about anything apart from the vague possibility of imminent nausea.

Dougal, Dylan, Florence, Brian and Ermintrude all like to sit on The Magic Roundabout. So do the children, Coral and Basil. Even Mr Rusty has been known to take a spin or two. Only Zebedee has never been seen on a horse, and that's only because he hasn't got any legs and can't hold on properly.

The Magic Roundabout is just like all those rides you remember from the funfairs of your childhood, except that you don't have to pay a fortune to get on it and it's not run by a man who looks like an ex-convict.

But The Magic Roundabout holds a terrible secret, a secret that has been kept for ten thousand years. Far, far below the Roundabout, in a volcanic cavern full of molten rock, a blue-skinned, wicked enchanter has been imprisoned, for the terrible crime of trying to freeze the sun. Since the day of his captivity he works ceaselessly, tirelessly at plans of escape.

Unfortunately one day, he succeeds, thanks to a careless dog and some sweets…

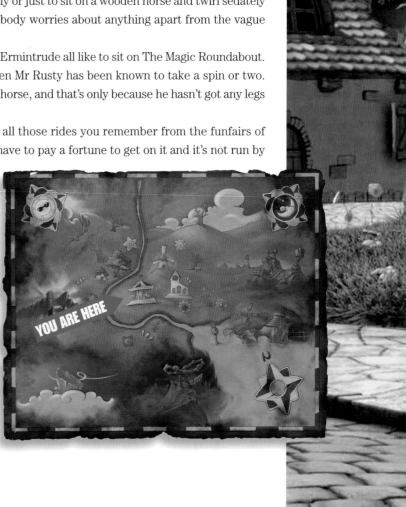

YOU ARE HERE

An Enchanted Beginning
The History of the Springers

Back in the mists of prehistory, in the days when ancient temples were built and tunnels dug through solid rock, when train tracks were laid across vertiginous bridges and huge statues were carved out of the sides of mountains, back in the days before The Magic Roundabout itself, a race of powerful jack-in-the-boxes lived in the Enchanted Land.

Known as Springers because they had springs instead of legs (it was a peculiarly literal time) they bounded around the landscape, taking care of those less powerful than themselves. They could perform magical feats, create balls of fire in the palms of their hands and shoot beams of pure energy from their luxuriant moustaches. They acted as mentors, guides, teachers and friends. They looked after everyone and they used their amazing powers to do good.

All except for the one named Zeebad (as you might expect, given his name).

Zeebad wanted power. Zeebad wanted respect. Zeebad wanted to instil fear in those who looked upon him and see them flinch at the slightest mention of his name. And, most of all, Zeebad wanted the Enchanted Land to be frozen, cold as ice. No trees. No flowers. No fluffy bunnies. Balaclavas and scarves for all.

When Zeebad tried to take control of the Enchanted Land, it fell to a young Springer named Zebedee to stop him. Zebedee was the ideal Springer: kind, warm and helpful (if slightly aloof). And, of course, pretty bouncy. He alone stood in Zeebad's way. Perhaps the

'So we meet again.'
Zebedee

two of them had once been friends, companions, even brothers. Perhaps they even played on the same basketball team – we may never know. Whatever the truth, Zebedee never talks about it now. But they fought.

Their confrontation shook the very rock, sending mountains falling into the sea and tidal waves crashing over tropical islands. With titanic energies being thrown back and forth, scorching their moustaches and damaging even the two near-immortal Springers themselves. Eventually, Zebedee was victorious, and Zeebad lay unconscious.

Using three magic diamonds to strip the wicked Springer of his powers, Zebedee imprisoned Zeebad in a volcanic cavern, surrounded by a lake of lava and pinioned by stalactites and stalagmites. Over the top of the cavern Zebedee created a Magic Roundabout, and he set himself the task of always remaining nearby, guarding the Enchanted Land against the day Zeebad might eventually escape.

For 10,000 years all was peaceful.

As the time rolled past, the Springers gradually vanished from the Enchanted Land. Eventually Zebedee and Zeebad were the only ones left. In the intervening years, the Enchanted Land had become home to others: dogs, rabbits, snails, cows and people. They came to regard Zebedee as their protector, although he never let on what he was protecting them against.

Until the day that Zeebad escaped. For the first time in living memory, even Zebedee was afraid. He knew what Zeebad was capable of, and he knew that with 10,000 years of imprisonment, Zeebad's thirst for vengeance would be insatiable. Zebedee would have to face his old nemesis once again…

'I hoped this day would never come!'
Zebedee

Basil and Coral

Basil and Coral are children who live in the Enchanted Village. They are friends with Dougal, Florence and the rest of the people and animals who spend their time on or near The Magic Roundabout.

All day they play games, help out and generally enjoy themselves, instead of doing the usual things kids do like covering The Magic Roundabout in graffiti and tying fireworks to Dougal's tail (if they could find it).

When Ermintrude throws her regular musical soirées, Basil and Coral are always there to cheer her on. They know she can't sing to save her life, but they don't want to hurt her feelings. After all, Ermintrude is their friend.

Life in the Enchanted Village is usually happy and peaceful, but when Zeebad escapes from the cavern in which he has been imprisoned in for 10,000 years, Basil and Coral's

playground is suddenly turned into something more like a battleground. Zeebad's dark enchantments turn The Magic Roundabout into an ice-bound prison, and neither Basil nor Coral can escape.

As the temperature drops and icicles begin to form, the children get more and more scared. Florence tries comforting them, but she is also scared. As time passes, Basil and Coral start to wonder if they will ever get out of their frozen cage…

Brian

The Enchanted Village is home to many creatures: cows, rabbits, dogs, people – and one rather large mollusc. They each bring their own particular characteristics to the Village. If Dougal is the impulsive side of the Village and Florence its heart then Brian the Snail is the Village's voice of reason. A still, small voice, but definitely a voice.

Brian is Rather Keen On:

Ermintrude's singing
Ermintrude's face
Ermintrude's sweet sweet smile
Ermintrude's tail
Ermintrude's poise and elegance

Brian, like Ermintrude, wears a hat and scarf and little else, although if the weather gets a little inclement he can always retreat inside his shell. He has a cosy little nest in there, with electric lights, toothbrush and full bathroom facilities. Brian enjoys carrying out little DIY tasks inside his shell, and often spends entire weekends watching paint dry.

Like any snail, Brian doesn't move terribly fast. In fact, he's the slowest inhabitant of the Enchanted Village (with the exception of Dylan when he's asleep). He manages to keep up with his friends by sliding along the ground, leaving a trail of slime behind him – a less than endearing habit which helps explain why the interior of his shell isn't carpeted. When pressed, however, he can manage a substantial turn of speed – at least, in his own eyes.

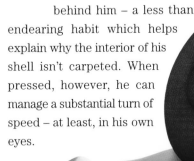

To everyone else it looks as if he is just sliding slightly less slowly than before.

Brian has a secret, which he keeps from the rest of his friends in the Enchanted Village. He has fallen in love with Ermintrude. Unfortunately, he is keeping it a secret from her as well. He cares about her to the point where he is the only person in the entire Village who believes that Ermintrude can actually sing in tune (well, the only person apart from her). Brian is forever trying to work up the courage to tell her of his feelings, but his snail-like timidity means that he stammers and stutters and finds it difficult to get to the point. On the few occasions when he does manage to get all the right words in the right order he realizes that Ermintrude has either misunderstood what he is saying or something happens to hijack the conversation. Like an insane wizard with blue skin attempting to freeze the sun. That kind of thing. Could happen to anyone.

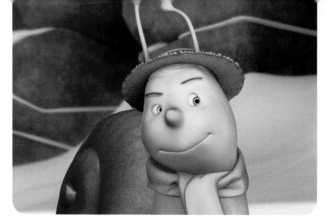

Despite the fact that Brian is small and does not possess a backbone, he can be surprisingly courageous at times. When the wicked magician Zeebad escapes from the Magic Roundabout and uses his ancient powers to bring ice and snow to the Enchanted Village, Brian is one of the first to join the quest to seek out the three magic diamonds that can stop

'It's so cold – I can't feel my limb.'
Brian

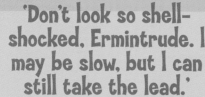

'Don't look so shell-shocked, Ermintrude. I may be slow, but I can still take the lead.'
Brian

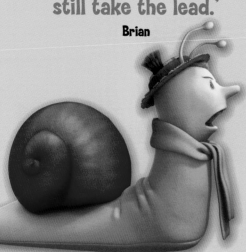

Brian's alternative shells

The Gothic

The Grand

The Mystic

The Rural

Zeebad in his tracks and send him back into eternal imprisonment. And he never gives up. Ever.

He also helps out when Dougal is kidnapped by Zeebad. Ermintrude is lowered into Zeebad's cavern and manages to rescue Dougal from his cage, but the two of them are spotted by Zeebad as they attempt to escape. Zeebad springs upwards and grabs Ermintrude's tail, but Brian – incensed at this treatment of his *inamorata* – ties a rope to his own tail and plummets down to where Zeebad has grabbed Ermintrude and bites hard on Zeebad's wrist without a moment's thought. Zeebad grabs hold of the dangling Brian by the scarf, dragging him closer to the ground and stretching his tail to the point where Dylan could probably get a decent tune out of it, but Brian's inherent elasticity snatches him back out of the magician's grasp.

Later, when Ermintrude, Dougal and Dylan are considering giving up after it looks like Zeebad has taken the life of their mentor Zebedee, Brian is the one who talks them into continuing, despite the fact that they may not make it all the way. During the fight with the skeletal Ninja warriors who are guarding the ancient temple wherein the second magic diamond is hidden, Brian bites the ankle of one of them when it goes to menace Ermintrude. And when the companions are attempting to get into an ancient temple which is protected by all kinds of booby-traps, Brian slides right in and sets off all the traps, but manages to avoid falling boulders, hurtling arrows and all kinds of fatal events. To be fair, he is distracted by his rant about how everyone takes him for granted, but it's the thought that counts.

During one of the most exciting parts of the quest, when Brian, Dougal, Ermintrude and Dylan are hurtling across narrow bridges on their Magic Train while being chased by the pitiless Zeebad, Brian is accidentally flung into the air when Dylan presses the ejector seat button, and he ends up perched on top of Zeebad's horrifying Mole Train. Momentarily stunned, and with his scarf in his eyes, Brian thinks he has landed back on the Magic Train. He asks whether they've managed to

Sometimes Brian felt like he was carrying the entire world on his shoulders...

Brian can't be doing with:

Garlic butter
People being rude to Ermintrude
Being taken for granted
Salt
Being told to come out of his shell

'Sam, get out the garlic butter. I'm feeling a little peckish.'
Zeebad

escape back to The Magic Roundabout yet, but thanks to his careless words Zeebad suddenly realizes where the last magic diamond is located. Rescued by Ermintrude, Brian has to admit shamefully that he has given the game away and almost certainly allowed Zeebad to triumph.

At their lowest point, when Zeebad has obtained all the magic diamonds and is about to use their power to freeze the sun, Brian and his friends return to the Enchanted Village. They watch, despondently, as Zeebad casts his dark magic, but Dylan suddenly decides he won't take it any more, and throws a snowball at Zeebad. His concentration broken, Zeebad turns on the friends, and together they distract him for long enough to retrieve the diamonds and return them to their rightful place on The Magic Roundabout. Brian plays his part, using his muscular 'foot' as a snowboard while performing stunt tricks in order to keep Zeebad from snatching the diamonds back. Truly a heroic snail.

And yet, despite everything, he still can't tell Ermintrude how he feels.

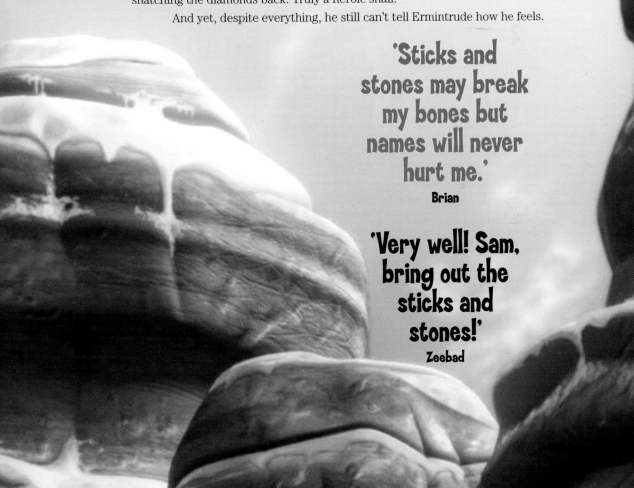

'Sticks and stones may break my bones but names will never hurt me.'
Brian

'Very well! Sam, bring out the sticks and stones!'
Zeebad

The Candy Seller

Everyone is happy in the Enchanted Village, and one of the things that makes them happiest is the Candy Seller. A friendly chap, he has a shop near the village square, from which he dispenses gobstoppers, fudge, sherbets, caramel crèmes, lollipops and every imaginable kind of sweet.

When he is not at his shop, the Candy Seller can be found pootling round the Enchanted Village on his motorized tricycle. With a large hamper at the front where he stores his wares, the tricycle is the perfect way for him to get around.

Much of the Candy Seller's merchandise is monopolized by Dougal the Dog. Dougal has a fondness for sugar, and he doesn't necessarily want to barter for it either. He thinks the Candy Seller should be giving the sweets away. Just before Zeebad's escape from The Magic Roundabout, Dougal sabotages the Candy Seller's tricycle by putting a thumb tack in the middle of the road. When the tricycle stops, Dougal claims it's a major mechanical failure and cunningly sends the rather gullible Candy Seller into the Enchanted Village to look for spares. While the Candy Seller is gone Dougal raids the hamper for sweets. The trouble is, Dougal is unfamiliar with the controls and accidentally manages to set the tricycle going. The tricycle careers through the village and ends up crashing into The Magic Roundabout, setting Zeebad free. Armageddon is nigh, and all because of a few gobstoppers and lollipops…

Disaster strikes, in the form of an innocent little thumb tack.

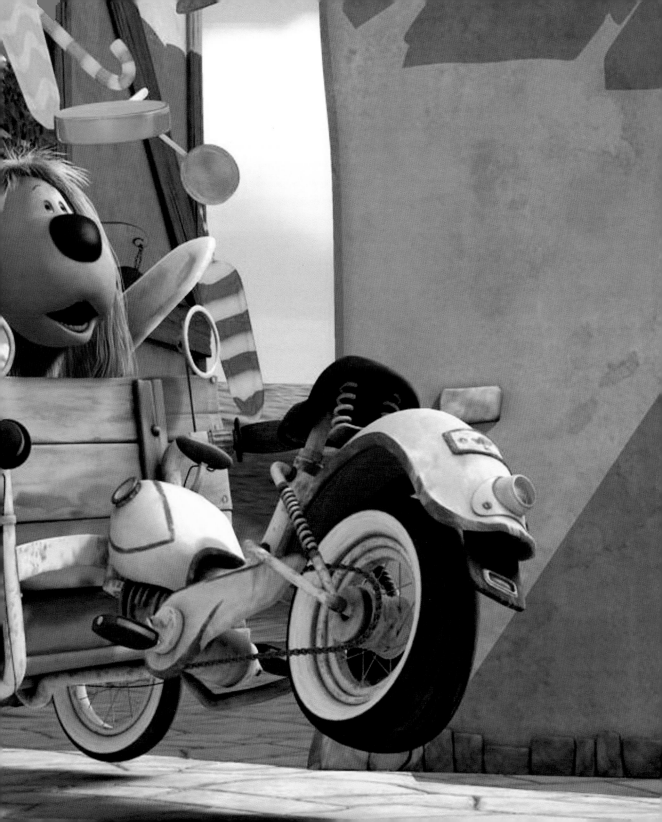

Dougal

'I'll not rest until I've done everything in my power to bake things right...'
Dougal

Below: The mighty hunter stalks his prey – the elusive chocolate bon-bon.

Petty but heroic, greedy but surprisingly unselfish on occasions, pompous but loveable, Dougal is a dog of contradictions. He thinks of himself as the leader of the inhabitants of the Enchanted Village (leading from the rear, of course), but most of the problems the Village faces are his fault in the first place.

Whilst some of the inhabitants of the Enchanted Village only speak when they have something to say, Dougal maintains what sometimes seems like a continual stream of conversation. He talks to his friends, he talks to people he has never met before and, when all else fails, he talks to himself. He doesn't talk to the trees, of course, otherwise they would put him away.

You can't mistake Dougal for anyone else in the village. He's the only dog in a community of people, molluscs, farmyard animals and wild creatures and his long sandy hair and chubby face instantly mark him out from the crowd. He's often to be seen with his tongue hanging out, panting for breath, but nobody is ever sure whether this is because he exercises so strenuously or because he is so frequently overcome by his desire for food.

Dougal's main characteristic is his greed. He loves sugar. He will eat it in the form of sweets – gobstoppers, sherbets, caramel crèmes and lollipops – but if he cannot get sweets then he will go straight for the pure stuff: sugar cubes.

'I think I'll take care of those lollipops first...'
Dougal

He can eat them until the cows (well, Ermintrude at least) come home. If he could, he would live on sugar and nothing else.

Dougal's love of sugar is so overpowering, and his willpower is so weak, that he has been known to hijack the Candy Seller who trundles about the village on his motorized tricycle. In fact, it is because of Dougal and the tricycle that the cruel Zeebad escapes from his prison beneath The Magic Roundabout.

Desperate to correct his mistake, Dougal sets off with his friends Brian, Ermintrude and Dylan, to find the three magic diamonds that will help Zebedee imprison Zeebad, and make the Enchanted Village green again. Even in the midst of this serious quest, however, Dougal's greed gets the better of him. In a temple on a tropical island, whilst his companions are avoiding deadly booby-traps in

Dougal's Greatest Loves

~~Suger~~ Florence
~~Sugah~~ Friends
Shuger
Shuggar
Suga

30

order to get one of the diamonds, Dougal accidentally spits a gobstopper out, triggering a trap that releases the diamond's guardians.

Strangely, for one who spends so much time complaining about being uncomfortable and trying to avoid anything remotely courageous or dangerous, it's often Dougal who manages to motivate them and get them back on track when the chips are down and everyone is morose and on the verge of giving up. Twice, during the quest to save the Enchanted Village from the fiendish Zeebad, Dougal gives a pep-talk to his friends and companions, pushing them onward. Dougal likes to give the impression that he has only his own interests at heart, but his reaction when Zebedee is being menaced by Zeebad reveals his true courage, for while Brian, Ermintrude and Dylan are prepared to run away, it is Dougal who wants to go back and help.

'I only wanted to get my
teeth into some sweeties.'
Dougal

> **'Help! Dogs are meant to eat bones – not the other way around!'**
> Dougal

Dougal's Least Favourite Things

Diets, particularly those involving sugar-free anything
Work
Disappointing Florence
Ermintrude's concerts
Aspartame

Even in Dougal's darkest moment, when it seems as though Zeebad has won and the Enchanted Village will be buried under ice forever, he still can't help thinking about sweets. Exhausted and afraid, lost in the snow, he slips into a bizarre dream (see Dougal's Dream). And, in the end, it is Dougal's bravery and courage, not to mention his unerring ability to throw a magic jewel on top of The Magic Roundabout, that win the day.

Dougal's relationship with Florence is the single best thing in his life. She is his closest friend, and the person he most hates to disappoint. His earliest memory is of Florence throwing a tennis ball for him to catch, and when Florence is imprisoned on The Magic Roundabout by Zeebad's cruel sorcery Dougal promises that he will fight to the bitter end to save her. There's a bond that exists between them: one that is often stretched by Dougal's general unreliability and Florence's exasperation, but one that will never be broken.

'Sugar?
Who needs
sugar?
Not me!
I quit! This
morning!'
Dougal

Dougal's Dream

Dougal's a very rational dog. He's not given to flights of fancy or hallucinations. He's not the Enchanted Land's most imaginative inhabitant. In fact, he tends to pooh-pooh that kind of thing, especially when it comes from Dylan.

So when he does actually experience a vivid dream, it worries him. He's well aware that it's probably his guilty conscience trying to persuade him to change his naughty ways (either that or a carbohydrate-induced hallucination). Not that he normally lets anything as insubstantial as a dream stop him from doing what he wants, but it nags at him. It makes him irritable and snappy.

Well, more irritable and snappier. It's not like he's a saint all the time.

At the lowest point of their quest for the magic diamonds, when they have lost their transport and bearings and are trudging aimlessly through the snowy wastes, Dougal and his three friends all fall prey to tiredness and tumble into sleep. And Dougal, in particular, has a very strange dream…

He dreams that he is standing on a path made of sugar cubes in a magical candy-filled world. Sweets float past, almost begging him to eat them. Everything is bright and colourful. Florence is there, even though he knows she's slowly freezing back on The Magic Roundabout. In his dream, however, she's laughing and calling to

'You can eat
as much as
you like!'
Florence

'Don't worry, Dougal. You're with me, in sugar paradise!'

A thick blanket of snow isn't as comfortable as it sounds.

eat them. Suddenly there are four Florences, all throwing sweets at Dougal. The quartet run down the sugar-cube path, calling to him, luring him on, throwing sweets to and fro above his head, just out of his reach…

Dougal wakes with a start. He knows that Florence wouldn't act like that towards him. She hates it when he pigs himself on sugar and sweets. She's always trying to get him to stop. He cries out in anguish and sadness for what he may soon lose, and the rest of his companions wake up, confused. Energized by his dream, and knowing that Florence depends on him, Dougal presses them on…

'Strange – for a second there I thought I heard… I must be going mad.'

Florence

Dougal's Vision

Dougal is usually the most practical of dogs – if he can't eat it or talk to it then he's not really interested – but occasionally he gets visions of a world beyond the mundane or even the sugary.

When he approaches the first magic diamond, Dougal finds himself having a vision of what's happening back in the Enchanted Village. Dougal sees his best friend Florence trapped on The Magic Roundabout, with Mr Rusty and the two children, Basil and Coral. Ice is

'Florence! It's me, Dougal! I'm going to save you!'

creeping up their legs, freezing them in place, and Florence is doing her best to stop the two children from getting scared. Mr Rusty is using his trusty spanner to try and free them from the grip of the ice, but all he does is bring icicles raining down on their heads.

The vision fades, leaving Dougal more determined than ever to find the rest of the magic diamonds and save his friends...

Dylan

'Woah, don't toast the hamsters, dude.'
Dylan

Of all the creatures in the Enchanted Village, Dylan the rabbit's the one who most clearly sees the beauty and the wonder all around him. And often a lot that's only in his head. He lives for the moment, rarely feeling bad about the past or worrying about the future. He has enough problems keeping track of the present.

Dylan seems to spend a lot of his time asleep. In fact, it's like he's in a perpetual state of semi-hibernation. He can fall asleep at the slightest opportunity, regardless of what he happens to be doing at the time. He might be playing guitar on stage or fighting a group of deadly Ninja Skeletons, but his head will start nodding, his ears will start drooping and his eyes begin to close. He's off, dreaming about things that only spaced-out rabbits can understand. He can even fall asleep while he's asleep, which is a pretty neat trick.

'Don't fret' has always been Dylan's motto.

Like many a hippy (and, let's face it, he *is* a hippy), Dylan is under the impression that he can play the guitar. But unlike most hippies, he actually can. If he can be bothered to stay awake for long enough then his fingers fly across those strings, pumping out squealing feedback and massive power chords to accompany his friend Ermindude's rather more restrained operatic singing. He can't manage it for long, however, and he usually ends up slumped back over his instrument like a clapped-out folk singer.

When Dougal confesses that he eats rather a lot of sugar, Dylan knows where the dog is coming from. 'It starts with some sweets, maybe an iced bun, and before you know it you're on two bags of sugar a day,' he points out. 'Maybe you've got a problem, my furry friend.' Later, when Dylan, Ermintrude, Brian and Dougal are stranded while searching for the magic diamonds, Dylan remembers that he has 'something stashed that just might help'. Brian misunderstands before realizing that Dylan is talking about a magic box given to him by Zebedee. And finally, when the Village is freed from its icy prison, Dylan is overjoyed to see 'sweet, green grass' all around him. A nature-lover, obviously.

'I'm in a higher state of unconsciousness.'
Dylan

Zebedee explains the intricacies of the remote control device to Dylan. Again.

'This guy
is seriously messing
with my karma.'
Dylan

Despite his apparent dopiness and sleepiness, and the fact that his friends tend to treat him as something of a joke, Dylan is the one who is trusted by Zebedee with the box that can change the Magic Train's shape (perhaps he thinks that Dylan's the one who will be least worried by things changing size and shape in front of him). Zebedee obviously sees qualities in Dylan that the others have missed, although, to be fair, Dylan can't work out how to operate the magic box, even though it only has one large button on it.

In fact, Dylan is capable of surprising everyone, and does so on many occasions during their quest. When the four companions have to get across a boiling pit of lava to a volcanic peak to find the first magic diamond, it's Dylan – the spaced-out narcoleptic – who drives the Magic Train across the narrow rock causeway, and when the Train almost slips off the causeway and falls into the lava, it's Dylan who manages to steer it back onto the straight and narrow. When they all need to escape from the volcanic peak, and discover that all the magic box does is

'Cool light show, man. Hello pretty lasers.'

turn the Train's wagon into a boat, it's Dylan who realizes that they can stitch their tents together and use the steam from the Train's funnel to inflate them into a balloon. He also has a way of spotting things that the others tend to miss, possibly because he sees everything through innocent, non-judgemental (albeit sleepy) eyes. At the beginning of their quest to save The Magic Roundabout, when Dougal is abducted by Zeebad, Brian and Ermintrude are looking for any tracks that he might have left, but it's Dylan who spots the large blue moose that's standing nearby – a moose that knows where Dougal is being held prisoner. He probably just thinks it's one of his unusual dreams. And when the four companions are floating above a vast ocean, unsure which way to go to find the second magic diamond, it's Dylan who sees the tiny figures of Zeebad and Soldier Sam rowing far below and who suggests following them. Dylan appears to see things that everyone else dismisses as being too obvious to mention. Or perhaps he just sees things. It could go either way.

Sometimes, Dylan feels like singing the Blues...

Stuff That Dylan Digs

Grass (basic foodstuff)

Watership Down (gives rabbits a good name)

Gadgets with simple instructions

Loud guitar solos

Sleep

'Woah – bad trip.'
Dylan

Like most rabbits, Dylan is essentially peace-loving and timid. He doesn't believe in violence – unless he or his friends are attacked. Then he can turn in an instant into a deadly fighting machine, displaying an intimate knowledge of 'kung-fu, karate, judo, kendo, tai-kwan-do, anything-you-can do, and tai-chi'. Attacked by four Ninja Skeletons, Dylan manages to keep them at bay with an impressive display of chops, kicks and throws.

As well as taking on the four Ninja Skeletons, Dylan also sees fit to take on the mighty magician Zeebad as well. When all looks lost for the Enchanted Village and The Magic Roundabout, when Zeebad has gained control over the three magic diamonds and is using them to freeze the sun, when Zebedee is presumed dead and the rest of the brave companions have given up all hope, Dylan finally loses his temper. Scooping up a handful of snow from the ground, and regardless of the danger, the not-so-happy hoppy hippy throws a snowball directly at Zeebad, enraging the magician and sparking off a chain of events that cause Zeebad to lose control of the magic diamonds, which leads to his defeat. Dylan didn't even know what he was doing – he just did it, and it all turned out OK. How typical.

Opposite: The fight against Zeebad promises to be a Titanic struggle.

Stuff That Dylan Doesn't Dig

Anything that involves effort
Attacks on his friends
Blue-faced megalomaniacs
Mr MacGregor
'Bright Eyes' (gives rabbits a bad name)

'OK people –
we've got a
problem.'
Dylan

Ermintrude

Meaty, beaty, big and bouncy – that's the best way to describe Ermintrude. She's a whole lot of cow with a whole lot of attitude and very little in the way of self-awareness. But she's brave and she means well, and that's what really counts.

What's the first thing that strikes you about Ermintrude? Well, to be honest it's usually her tail. Or her hoof if she's particularly annoyed. Ermintrude doesn't like to be ignored, and she has a way of showing her displeasure in a way that leaves an impression. And several bruises.

OK, what's the second thing that strikes you about Ermintrude? It's probably her love of music. She venerates Verdi, worships Wagner and feels passionate about Puccini (although she's strangely ambivalent about Albinoni). She also trained as a ballet dancer, and she firmly believes she can not only sing as

Ermintrude's Top Five Things

Anything about the Rich and Famous

All classical music

Architecture

Bringing a touch of class to her friends' drab lives

Performing

Ermintrude – the cow who came in from the cold
Inset: Rump steak – very tasty

'Puccini
preserve
us!'
Ermintrude

beautifully as Pavarotti but dance as lithely as a cat, although the sad truth is she sings like a cat and dances like Pavarotti. She can't hit a note without breaking it, but that doesn't stop her from organizing concerts in the Enchanted Village, with Dylan and Mr Rusty accompanying her on guitar and musical box respectively. All of her friends turn up to the concerts to demonstrate their love for her, but they can't help but wince at the noise she makes.

Her friends are just grateful there's only one Ermintrude.

It has to be said that Ermintrude's mistaken belief in her own musical abilities has clouded her bovine mind to the extent that she thinks that she's in a class above her friends and companions. She still loves them, of course, but not as equals. More like amusing social inferiors. She's clearly the *vache sans pareil* of the Enchanted Village. When Zebedee produces a Magic Train for Ermintrude and her friends to travel in, for instance, the first thing she asks is whether it has First Class accommodation (entirely oblivious to the fact that she should be travelling Cattle Class).

Although she doesn't realize it, Ermintrude has a secret admirer. Brian the Snail has long held a torch for her (but not against her, which would be the quickest route to a medium rare steak). He's desperately trying to screw up the courage to come out of his shell and tell her how he feels. Alas, something always happens to prevent him taking the cow by the horns (as it were), and Ermintrude will probably never know. She does have a soft spot for Brian, however – when he is threatened with a good basting in garlic butter by the nefarious Zeebad she stands up for him, and when he is trapped on top of Zeebad's Mole

Opposite: Moo-moo-moo-moo, stayin' alive!

Ermintrude's Favourite Films

Under Milk Wood
Cattle Queen of Montana
The Udders
Raging Bull
Anything starring Cowtherine Zeta Jones or John Herd

Train, hurtling at great speed across narrow bridges and in imminent danger of falling to his death, she uses her tail to pull him to safety.

Despite being a hefty heifer, Ermintrude can still just about cut the mustard in the dance department when the chips are down and the stakes are high (although steak and chips with mustard are not something you want to mention too loudly when she's around). During the quest to find the three magic diamonds and defeat the evil wizard Zeebad, when Ermintrude, Brian, Dougal and Dylan are trapped in an ancient temple by a startlingly sophisticated web of laser beams, Ermintrude uses her dancer's flexibility to move over, under

'It's hardly the Orient Express. Does it have First Class?'
Ermintrude

'This is too Wagnerian for words!'
Ermintrude

and around them until she can reach the magic diamond at the centre of the web. One false move and she would have been diced, sliced and lightly seared on all sides – from terror to teriyaki in one easy lesson.

Surprisingly, given her selfish ways, Ermintrude can be amazingly brave when her friends are in danger. When Dougal is kidnapped by Zeebad and imprisoned in an ice cage, it's Ermintrude who's lowered through a hole in the roof of Zeebad's cage to rescue the dog (falling on Soldier Sam and nearly crushing him in the process). Similarly, when the four companions are being menaced by Ninja Skeletons in an ancient temple, Ermintrude steps forward and smacks one of the Ninjas in the face with her hoof, sending it flying across the temple floor. She may be a cow, but she's no coward.

Above: A look of udder surprise. Below: Ermintrude looks stern. Or is it astern?

Despite her obvious reluctance to go join the quest to stop Zeebad, Ermintrude plays a key role in keeping the little band of travellers together, and also, later, in defeating the malicious magician. At the end of their long and arduous journey, when she discovers the Enchanted Village is completely snow-bound, Ermintrude uses her horribly off-key voice to shatter the ice that's holding her friends captive. She also uses her dancer's skills to keep the last of the magic diamonds out of Zeebad's clutches for long enough so that her friends

can restore it to its natural place on top of The Magic Roundabout. Without Ermintrude, they all would have faced disaster and the Enchanted Village would have been subject to an eternal winter (although you'd think she would be used to Friesian conditions, wouldn't you?).

When the chips are down, Ermintrude always comes through. She's a real trouper, and no bull.

'Now, for my next number...'
Ermintrude

Ermintrude's Concert

In the middle of the Enchanted Village, near The Magic Roundabout, there is a plain wooden stage. Not ornate, not fiddly at all. Not particularly grand. It has been, however, the scene of some of Ermintrude's greatest performances. And, it has to be said, some of her worst.

Every now and then, as the mood takes her, she decides to give a recital in the village. Posters are printed, tickets sold, and an air of expectation (not to mention lurking dread) stirs in the hearts of the Enchanted Village's many inhabitants.

One the day that Zeebad escapes from the fiery cavern in which Zebedee had imprisoned him 10,000 years ago, Ermintrude is hosting another of her recitals. Mr Rusty and Dylan are providing the music on guitar and music box. Florence is there in the audience, watching, as are the two children, Basil and Coral, and Brian the Snail (who has bought flowers for Ermintrude – a nice gesture, as it turns out, because she is a bit peckish).

After a slight delay caused by the fact that Dylan has fallen asleep, Ermintrude begins the recital. Her first piece is the toreador's song from Bizet's opera *Carmen*. It starts well, if you're willing to accept the fact that Ermintrude is horribly out of tune, but things start to slide when Dylan begins to nod off. Ermintrude notices, and clips him round the head with her tail. Stunned, Dylan launches into a number of his own, which neither Ermintrude nor Mr Rusty can keep up with. Dylan plays on and on, fingers flickering faster and faster over the strings of his guitar, and just as it looks as if his guitar will catch fire due to the heat of his playing the concert is brought to a complete standstill when Dougal the dog crashes a tricycle into The Magic Roundabout...

Opposite: It's just a stage she's going through...

Ermintrude's Pet Peeves

Schoenberg and any music involving vacuum cleaners

Heights, particularly being left dangling over them

Singing cows in adverts

The cold

Sweet wrappers and mobile phones going off in performances

Florence

'Come on then everyone – to the Roundabout!'

Florence

Somewhere in between a dopey rabbit, a selfish dog, a pompous cow and a nervous snail there's a sensible girl, trying (with some exasperation) to get everyone to play together nicely.

Florence's closest friend is Dougal, the sugar-obsessed dog. They've known each other since Dougal was just a puppy. In fact, his earliest memory is of Florence throwing a ball for him. Florence is often irritated at Dougal's antics, but she loves him really, and he loves her. Similarly, Dougal tries his hardest not to disappoint Florence, but sometimes he just can't help himself.

Florence is the calm centre of the Enchanted Village. Rather than follow her emotions or react without thinking when everything starts to go wrong, she's the one who tries to work out what's the best thing to do. And then she watches, calmly of course, as everyone else rushes off and panics.

When Dougal's antics on an out-of-control tricycle cause damage to The Magic Roundabout and allow the wicked Zeebad to escape, Florence is trapped on the Roundabout by Zeebad's icy powers. While the Roundabout grows colder and colder, Florence tries to keep up the spirits of her fellow captives – Mr Rusty and the children Basil and Coral – by playing games and talking reassuringly. Although she is worried about the increasing cold, Florence knows that Dougal and the rest of her friends will rescue them all, even without her sensible supervision.

'Don't worry children – our friends will save us!'

Florence

59

YOU ARE HERE

The Frozen Mountainside

*The Enchanted Land isn't just a land of flowers and fields
and bunny-wunnies, it's a land of contrasts. It has tropical
islands and volcanic peaks.*

It has oceans and presumably deserts too. Miles of golden beaches and a vibrant
nightlife – the perfect place for a weekend break or a longer vacation. Who knows?
But one thing is for sure, not too far from the Enchanted Village it also has its
snowy mountain slopes, just perfect for tobogganing (especially if you're a snail).

The upper peaks of the mountains are frozen, jagged and steep, but their
lower slopes are really rather pleasant, and easily accessible by foot or Magic
Train. Fir trees cover the landscape, whilst moose wander around and nibble
their leaves, wondering what the plural of 'moose' might be. Ice tunnels lead to
all manner of interesting caves, one of which used to be the lair of sly Springer

Left: Not for the first time in his life, Dylan prepares for an in-tents experience.
Below: Even in the middle of a snowy wasteland, Ermintrude expects the best.

Zeebad (and became so again after Zeebad's escape from perpetual imprisonment, well semi-perpetual; given that he did actually escape).

The lower slopes of the mountains do have their dangers, however. Deep snow drifts can form unexpectedly if the wind gets up, and gradual slopes can end abruptly in sheer cliff faces. Unwary travellers can easily slip too far and slide over the edge, falling for thousands of feet into a crevice with little prospect of getting out again, unless of course they have springs instead of feet. The intense cold can also sap the strength, leading to tiredness, depression and hallucinations of sugar and sweets – as well as cold feet.

Although years can go by without anything happening on the mountain slopes, apart

from the occasional landslide and moose migration, they did provide the backdrop for a dramatic confrontation between the monstrous enchanter Zeebad and the good wizard Zebedee. Their titanic struggle sent energy bolts blasting everywhere, and resulted in the entire edge of a glacier falling into a crevice, taking Zebedee to his (presumed) final resting place. But after they had gone, and the echoes of their struggle had died away, the snowy mountain slopes remained, peaceful and cold. And the perfect location for a winter sports break.

The Magic Box

Zebedee always manages to come up with the right thing at the right time. Sometimes it's a spell, sometimes a kind word and sometimes a practical device that can solve all kinds of problems.

The Magic Box isn't exactly high-tech. It's just a box. A box with a single button on it. No instruction manual, no training course, just a box with a button. And yet, strangely, it still manages to confuse Dylan, who spends some time turning it over and over in his hands, trying to work out how to operate it. And that's despite the fact that Zebedee has already shown the four friends how it works.

When Dougal, Brian, Dylan, Ermintrude and the train are trapped above a lake of lava with their only way back to safety destroyed by the cruel Zeebad, Dylan desperately uses the Magic Box to change the Train into something that might help. Within moments, Train's wagon changes form – to a boat. The friends are about to give up when Dylan realises that they can tie their tents together and fill them with hot air, turning the Train into a balloon. Perhaps Zebedee knew what he was doing after all.

It's a box. A box with one button. How hard could it be?

The Magic Diamonds

Long before Florence, Dougal and the rest of the friends lived in the Enchanted Village, the immortal Springers Zebedee and Zeebad battled for control of the world.

Zebedee wanted everything to be warm and happy, but Zeebad wanted it to be frozen and unpleasant. Not much room for negotiation, you might think. Using three magic diamonds, Zeebad tried to recast the world the way he wanted it, but Zebedee thwarted his plans and used the magic diamonds to imprison Zeebad beneath The Magic Roundabout.

Zebedee scattered the magic diamonds far apart for fear that they might once again fall into the wrong hands, but when an unforeseen accident results in the cruel magician's escape the diamonds have to be found. They are, after all, a Springer's best friend.

The first diamond – the blue one – is hidden on top of a rocky crag in the centre of a volcanic pit. Access is by a narrow bridge, but only the most fearless of adventurers would cross it. Or, the most foolhardy.

The second diamond – the yellow one – is located on a remote island within an ancient temple dating back tens of thousands of years. The diamond is guarded by booby-traps and four

magical skeleton warriors whose sole purpose is to prevent any unauthorized attempts to remove it.

The third diamond – the red one – is hidden within the chest of a toy soldier which Zebedee set on top of The Magic Roundabout. Perhaps he wanted one of the diamonds close at hand, just in case he needed it. Or perhaps he just put it down and forgot where...

As far as Brian is concerned, nothing could be as beautiful as Ermintrude. Well, almost nothing...

The Magic Train

Dougal talks until he is blue in the face, Mr Rusty hardly speaks at all, but the Magic Train can speak volumes without saying a word. It communicates its moods and thoughts through its axles and wheels, its expressive headlight eyes and the puffs of white smoke that rise from its bright blue funnel.

The Magic Train is a personality in its own right, just as much as any other inhabitant of the Enchanted Village. And it's always there when they need it most.

When Zebedee calls together four of his friends – Dougal, Dylan, Brian and Ermintrude – and tells them that they must go on a quest to find the three magic diamonds, he knows he must give them a way of travelling across the Enchanted Land to the remote locations where the diamonds have been secreted. He asks the Magic Train to take them, and the

Train happily agrees. There's obviously not enough room in the driver's cab for everyone, so Zebedee also gives them a Magic Box that, at the push of a button, can provide a comfortable wagon behind the train into which they can all climb.

The friends set off in the Magic Train, puffing out of the Enchanted Village and across the Enchanted Land to their first destination. Along the way they stop for a night's rest. The Train, exhausted from its constant driving, falls asleep quickly.

The next day they arrive at the place where the first magic diamond has been hidden: a volcanic crag set in the middle of a pool of molten rock. Steam rises up from the hellishly hot lava below. All that links the ground they are standing on to the volcanic crag is an unstable causeway made of crumbling rock. Bravely, the Magic Train edges out across the causeway. The rock creaks and breaks beneath its weight, but the Train keeps on going. It almost falls off the bridge and into the lava when the rock crumbles directly beneath its wheels, but after what seems like an age, the Train and its passengers are safe on the other side. For the moment.

The friends find the first diamond, but the wicked Zeebad takes it away from them and destroys the bridge, stranding them on the volcanic crag. Fortunately, Dylan remembers the Magic Box and the Train's wagon transforms into a boat. With a bit of needlework they convert their tents into a balloon and use Train's steam to inflate it. After a short period of frantic activity they are rising serenely away from the rocky spire and on their way to the second diamond.

The location of the second diamond could not be more different. Instead of being on a bare spire, it can be found hidden in an ancient temple on an island covered by lush tropical vegetation. The Magic Train descends

upon the island from the skies. The landing would have been better if Dougal had not taken over navigation duties on the final approach. Train hits the ground hard, spilling its occupants every-which-where.

While the four friends find their way through the temple's corridors, the Train is left behind outside the entrance. Getting slightly nervous at being left alone, the Magic Train decides to follow the friends into the temple, but plunges through a concealed stone trapdoor and into a tunnel that has been carved out of the rock. Creeping through the dark tunnel the Train comes across another train – a fearsome Mole Train that has been left there by the long-dead makers of the ancient temple.

When the four friends find the second diamond they have to make a rapid escape, not just from the malicious Zeebad but also from a huge Ninja Skeleton that has been guarding the diamond. The Magic Train carries them rapidly through the dark tunnels of the temple, pursued by Zeebad in the Mole Train.

> 'Well, I hope you've supplied us with an appropriate mode of transportation.'
> **Ermintrude**

The two trains burst out of the darkened tunnels and onto a series of narrow bridges and tracks that span deep gorges. Time after time Zeebad attempts to plunge the mole Train's whirling drill into the Magic Train's wagon. Perilously the trains sway and clatter across the bridges – and then, disaster! Distracted when the Mole Train explodes, the Magic Train slams into a set of buffers, sending it and the four friends flying through the air to land in a pile of snow near the Enchanted Village. The Train has been damaged in the landing, and can now only limp. Sadly, it watches as the four friends continue their journey on foot.

Fortunately, all comes right in the end. Dougal, Brian, Ermintrude and Dylan defeat the monstrous Zeebad, with the help of a few friends, and Zebedee uses his magic powers to heal the Magic Train's wheel. Triumphantly it parades through the Enchanted Village, Everything is back to normal…

'Woah.
Looks like
this
service has
been
cancelled.'
Dylan

The Mole Train

Deep beneath an ancient temple, hidden in dark, cobwebbed tunnels, something sits patiently: The Mole Train.

Nobody knows who built the Mole Train – if, indeed, it was built, rather than conjured up in a sulphurous cloud of diesel fumes. Perhaps it was created by the builders of the temple, thousands of years before. Perhaps it was already there on the island when they arrived, a relic of some bygone age.

Unlike the cheerful, friendly Magic Train that Zebedee gives to his friends, the Mole Train is hauntingly vicious in appearance. Its construction is utilitarian and brutally industrial, and years of lurking in darkness have done nothing to improve its already sinister form. Its main feature is the huge rotating drill right at the front of the train (right where some trains have a cow-catcher, although this one is more likely to skewer a cow than catch it). Sharp enough to chew through solid rock, the drill enables the Mole Train's driver to create entirely new tunnels, rather than sticking to those that have already been dug. Forget being slowed by the wrong kind of leaves; this train can deal with solid rock!

When Zeebad and Soldier Sam confront Dougal, Ermintrude, Dylan and Brian in the ancient temple, Zebedee's four friends make their escape in their own Magic Train. Intent on finding out from them where the third and final magic diamond is located, Zeebad is ecstatic when he discovers the Mole Train beneath the temple's altar. Finally, after millennia of gathering dust, the Mole Train can be useful to someone again.

Opposite: Train now arriving on platform six is in a bit of a hurry!

'Sir – the pressure! It's too much!'
Soldier Sam

With Zeebad at the helm and Soldier Sam shovelling coal, the Mole Train speeds off in pursuit of the Magic Train. Years of neglect and disuse have taken their toll, however. The build-up of pressure in the Mole Train's creaky old boiler proves too much, and the seams give under the strain. Rivets pop, metal crumples, and the Mole Train explodes into a thousand metal fragments, flinging Zeebad and Soldier Sam head over heels through the air.

'Now, this is what happens if you don't brush regularly!'
Zeebad

The Moose

Somewhere far away from the Enchanted Village, out where the fields and hills run on to the horizon and the flowers bloom in wild and colourful profusion, there lives a moose.

A perfectly ordinary moose with a fine pelt of brown hair and a tremendous set of horns (which are only ever used for display and for digging up the occasional root). The moose never bothers the people who live in the Enchanted Village – all it asks is to be able to live in peace and quiet. He probably doesn't even know the Village exists.

And then Zeebad arrives.

Freed from his millennia-long imprisonment beneath The Magic Roundabout, Zeebad is in a foul mood. He wants to make everyone pay for what happened to him. He wants to freeze the sun and turn everything cold and icy.

The Moose is the first living creature that Zeebad sees when he is accidentally freed. Without even introducing himself, Zeebad fires a bolt of energy from the ends of his moustache, to test his magical abilities, but because his powers are a bit rusty he only succeeds in turning it blue. Satisfied that he's at least spoiled the moose's day, Zeebad goes on his nasty way.

The moose wanders forlornly for a while. Although it can still walk, and eat, and make moose-like noises, something isn't quite right. It misses its old colour. And the world is changing – becoming snowbound and cold. In some ways this suits the moose quite well – it had always felt a bit uncomfortable in the bright sunshine – but it prefers the green of the grass and the bright colours of the flowers.

The moose mooches around, wondering who might get things back to normal. After a while it meets travellers from the Enchanted Village who are off on a quest – a dog, a snail, a cow and a rabbit. The moose watches with concern as the dog is kidnapped by the wicked Zeebad, and as soon as it can the moose leads the dog's friends to where Zeebad is keeping him. The friends rescue the dog, and they go on their way. The moose mooches on, still blue, and alone once more.

After a while, the moose finds itself drawn towards the Enchanted Village. Perhaps meeting the snail, the rabbit, the dog and the cow has expanded its horizons, and it wants to see what else is out there. Perhaps it's just heading downhill and doesn't know where it's going. On the way, however, it discovers a badly damaged toy soldier lying on the ground. The moose rescues the soldier – that's the kind of moose it is – and together they head off towards the Enchanted Village.

They arrive just as the wicked Zeebad is attempting to freeze the sun using three magic diamonds. The toy soldier and the moose charge towards the magician, but he freezes the moose to the ground and nearly destroys the soldier. All looks lost, until the four friends the moose had met earlier rush in and confront Zeebad. They manage to take one of the diamonds and keep Zeebad from getting it. The dog flicks the third diamond into its position on The Magic Roundabout.

Everything is back to normal except for the moose, who is still blue. But even that gets sorted out when Zebedee, the good magician, returns. The moose is brown and surrounded by the scent of fresh flowers and green grass again. Simple pleasures for a brave beast.

The Railway Line

There are many unexplained things in the Enchanted Land. Ancient stone temples. Huge statues. The ruins of ancient civilizations. Mr Rusty's moustache. And an abandoned train line, built by some ancient hand, that plunges and swoops between tropical islands, mountain peaks and the mainland like some demented roller-coaster ride.

When Dylan, Brian, Ermintrude and Dougal, along with their faithful companion the Magic Train, reach the location of the second magic diamond in their quest to frustrate Zeebad's plans, they awaken an old evil. Chased by a large skeletal monster, they escape

along a dark old tunnel aboard their Magic Train. The tunnel is part of an old train system dating from some long-forgotten period of the Enchanted Land's history. They hope they can escape along the tracks. The relentless Skeleton tries to clamber aboard their Train, only to smash its skull on an overhanging rock, allowing the friends to get away.

The train tracks suddenly emerge from the dark tunnel into bright sunlight. The four companions and their faithful Train are surprised to find themselves hurtling across a narrow bridge, high above the sea. Other bridges emerge from dark holes in the cliff face behind them. Where do all these tracks go? What were they used for? What kind of trains used to trundle along them?

One of the answers to those questions is about to catch up with them....

'I can see the light at the end of the tunnel!'

Dylan

Above: for as long as he could remember – which is about half an hour – Dylan had always wanted to be a train driver. Right: Brian finds his life is suddenly back on track.

Mr Rusty

Although the Enchanted Village runs mainly on love, friendship and magic, there is still the occasional call for someone who is willing to get their hands dirty.

The town clock needs to be repaired every now and then, for instance, and the Candy Seller's tricycle motor often needs servicing. When there are gears to be stripped, oil to be drained or sparks to be plugged, the heavily moustachioed Mr Rusty is your man.

When he's not fiddling about inside an engine, Mr Rusty is prepared to spend the time making music with his friends. He's a dab hand with the old music box, and can often be found on the Enchanted Village's bandstand accompanying Ermintrude in a concert of operatic arias. Mr Rusty is quite happy to support his friends in this way, and has no great ambition to take centre stage. Providing quiet but invaluable support is what he does best.

'It's out of control!'
Mr Rusty

Soldier Sam

Soldier Sam is a decorative character on top of The Magic Roundabout, a carved wooden soldier in a smart red uniform who symbolically stands guard over all the children and animals who play there.

Along with other carved figures, like the ballerina, he is there in all weathers, night and day, never moving, never thinking. None of the people who play on The Magic Roundabout knows, however, that Soldier Sam is standing guard in a much more literal sense. He contains within him a secret that could spell disaster for the Enchanted Land and all its inhabitants.

When The Magic Roundabout breaks down and the wicked magician Zeebad is released from beneath it in a shower of sparks and ice, Soldier Sam is flung off the roof by the force and thrown through the air to land, far away, in a snowdrift. Zeebad lands nearby and, aware that he will need a henchman to help fight Zebedee and freeze the sun, decides to bring Soldier Sam to life. A blast from Zeebad's magical moustache expands Soldier Sam to towering size, which isn't quite what the nefarious magician wanted. Another blast reduces him to the same size as Zeebad and brings him to life. 'Soldier Sam, First Decorative Clockwork Regiment, Saaah!' he introduces himself. Zeebad is pleased with himself: now to conquer the Enchanted Land.

Soldier Sam isn't really cut out for the wicked life, however. Part of him dimly remembers the sound of the children laughing as they played on The Magic Roundabout, and the sight of the green grass and the multi-coloured flowers around the Enchanted Village, as glimpsed from his vantage point on top. Despite his loyalty to his master, he still yearns for peace and tranquillity and warmth. When Zeebad takes Sam to his old lair – an icy cavern inside a mountain – the first thing Sam wants to do is tidy up.

Opposite: Soldier Sam was beginning to realise that camouflage was not his strong suit.

He bustles around with a duster attempting to get the cave into some kind of order, humming happily to himself. And when Zeebad captures Dougal the dog and orders Sam to torture him to find out the location of the three magic diamonds he needs to freeze the sun, Sam is at a bit of a loss to know where to start. 'This is all a bit new to me,' he says to Dougal. Shortly after that he is flattened by a bovine rump as Ermintrude the cow arrives from above to rescue Dougal. Chasing the escapees out of the cavern, Sam follows Zeebad's instructions and menaces them all, but it's obvious his heart isn't in it.

Sam does try, however. He does his best to imitate Zeebad's insane cackling, although he can't quite manage the full effect. And when Zeebad bounces across a narrow rock causeway, having taken the first magic diamond from the four adventurers, Sam tries to bounce as well but only

'Faster, Sam! You row like a milkmaid!'
Zeebad

For a wooden soldier, a lantern is a worrying thing.

94

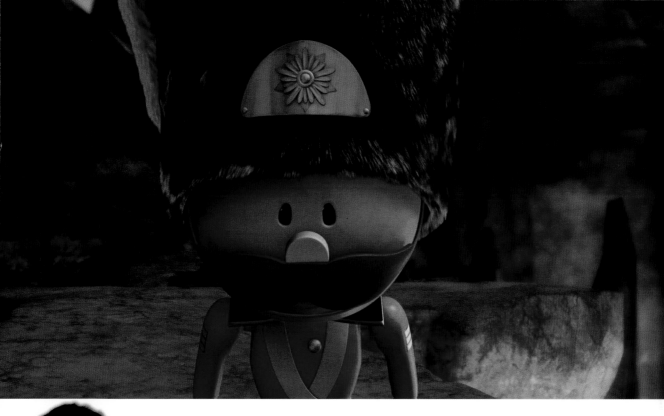

succeeds in breaking the causeway and marooning the adventurers. Later, as he rows Zeebad across the ocean towards the second diamond, Sam finds himself talking about Zeebad's motivations. 'Imagine,' Zeebad muses, 'if you'd waited 10,000 years to return to your frozen kingdom, only to find a worl d covered in flowers! And animals! And sunshine! And …' 'And trees, and rainbows, and tiny little bunnies…' Sam continues happily. Zeebad is not pleased.

When they get to the tropical island that houses the second magical diamond – with Sam having rowed all the way – they attempt to enter the ancient temple they find there, only for Sam almost to fall victim to a booby-trap that had been set up thousands of years before. Claiming to have a sixth sense about danger, Sam unfortunately steps on a flagstone, triggering a spring-loaded device that almost drives a wooden stake through his head. However, because the life of a toy soldier is full of danger, Sam reacts with admirable calm.

Zebedee's four friends also arrive at the temple, and a confrontation ends with them escaping from the temple in the Magic Train with Zeebad and Soldier Sam in hot pursuit in the relentless Mole Train. They hurtle across narrow bridges

'Sam, you're ruining the moment.'
Zeebad

95

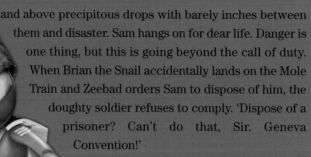

and above precipitous drops with barely inches between them and disaster. Sam hangs on for dear life. Danger is one thing, but this is going beyond the call of duty. When Brian the Snail accidentally lands on the Mole Train and Zeebad orders Sam to dispose of him, the doughty soldier refuses to comply. 'Dispose of a prisoner? Can't do that, Sir. Geneva Convention!'

Zeebad knows by now that Sam will never be the mindless follower he wants him to be, and so he dumps him at the next convenient opportunity. When the Mole Train crashes, leaving Sam badly injured, Zeebad refuses to use his magic to fix the soldier. Instead, he abandons him in the snow.

Sam is instead rescued by a moose, and makes his way

'You may wear a soldier's uniform, Sam, but it's what's inside that counts.'
Zebedee

painfully to The Magic Roundabout, where Zeebad is desperately searching for the third and final magic diamond. Sam confronts his former master, saying that he has come to his senses and should have been doing what he was built to do – guard The Magic Roundabout. Zeebad sneers, and fires a magical bolt from his moustache at the brave soldier. Sam collapses to the ground under the brunt of the magic energy, his chest splitting open to reveal the third diamond. Sam had unwittingly been its guardian all along! Zeebad takes the diamond and attempts to use all three to freeze the sun, but Zebedee's friends all turn up at the very last moment and, helped by a badly injured Sam, defeat the malicious magician and send him back to his eternal prison.

Zebedee appears, as he always does, and uses his own good magic to repair Sam and return him to his original size and position – guarding The Magic Roundabout against Zeebad's further escape.

> 'Good grief, you just can't get the staff these days.'
> **Zeebad**

The Secluded Temple

Somewhere far away from the Enchanted Village, past endless plains and volcanic peaks, across a vast sea, lies the ruins of an ancient civilization. These ruins date from the days when Zebedee and Zeebad first confronted one another. And it's in these ruins, overgrown by tropical vines and creepers, that the second of the magic diamonds was hidden, all those thousands of years ago.

'Hey man
– tropical
vibes.'
Dylan

The ruins of this ancient civilization can be found scattered across a range of mountainous islands which are clustered together somewhere in the middle of the vast sea. Enormous carvings of heads and feet dominate the landscape, remnants of some lost race of architects and craftsmen. The pinnacle of their craft is the massive temple that sits on top of the tallest mountain, on the largest island. Carved painstakingly from the rock, adorned by carvings and hieroglyphics, the temple also houses the second diamond deep in its heart.

Although the entrance to the temple may seem to be open, it's protected by its own fierce guardians. The plants that surround the way in may appear innocent, what with their succulent fruit and brightly coloured foliage, but they are actually carnivorous creatures which will attempt to take chunks out of anyone venturing too near. And even if the wary traveller manages to get past the plants, there are booby-traps and other guardians within… guardians even more sinister than the carnivorous plants…

The paved path that leads from the entrance of the temple to its dark interior contains hidden dangers. Some of the paving stones trigger booby-traps when they are stepped on. Arrows and spears are fired from hidden gaps; snakes drop from concealed holes and rocks plummet to the ground, crushing anyone beneath. Or is it that snakes are fired from hidden gaps, and arrows drop from concealed holes? Whatever: it takes rare gymnastic skill to avoid all these obstacles, or perhaps just a snail who isn't paying attention.

The heart of the temple is a throne room – a large, empty space panelled in gold and lit by flickering torches. In the centre of the throne room is – as one might expect – a throne, covered by the dust and cobwebs of 10,000 years. But the throne is another booby-trap, as Dougal finds out when he and his friends arrive there in search of the magic diamond and the self-centred dog decides to sit on the throne and enjoy his last

'A throne – the perfect place to enjoy my last gobstopper.'
Dougal

gobstopper. Seeing a button located conveniently in the arm of the stone throne, Dougal cannot resist pressing it. With a deafening grinding noise, a stone altar emerges from a concealed pit in the floor. In the centre of the altar the friends can see the magic diamond, but all the entrances are sealed with slabs of rock while beams of laser light cut across the floor, forming a web of light that, if broken, might seal their doom. And they can't get to the diamond without breaking one of the beams of laser light.

Except that whoever designed the booby-trap hadn't counted on a balletic cow...

The Skeleton Ninjas

Somewhere far out in the ocean, far from the Enchanted Village, lies a small island. On that island is a temple, an ancient place of decaying stone, rampant vegetation and yet, strangely, no booths selling tacky postcards and choc-ices.

In that temple lies one of the three magical diamonds that, together, possess the power to freeze the sun. And guarding that diamond are four immortal warriors – immortal, but not ageless, for long ago their flesh has crumbled from their bones, leaving only their skeletons intact.

Time has forgotten these warriors. They lie still, motionless beneath the massive stone slabs of the temple floor, waiting for that faint footfall, the slightest sound of flesh on stone that means that an intruder has breached the security of their sanctum. Nobody knows who they used to be. They probably don't even remember themselves. Bereft of

Make no bones about it, these things are dangerous.

names, of histories, of memories, all they do is lie still and wait.

They are the temple's last line of defence (actually, no, for there is one more trick the temple can pull if the four Skeleton warriors are defeated). They are summoned if the elaborate web of light beams that criss-cross the temple is broken by a person, an animal or a particularly unlucky gobstopper. And when that happens the floor opens up and they emerge, ready to fight.

When Dougal, Brian, Ermintrude and Dylan enter the temple in search of the second magic diamond, Dougal accidentally rouses the warriors when he spits his gobstopper out in a moment of high excitement and breaks the light beam. The warriors emerge, bones shining in the light from the flaming torches that line the temple walls, eye-sockets brooding darkly upon the many centuries they have waited to be summoned, joints creaking arthritically as they struggle to move. They cannot be stopped, they cannot be killed, and only one thing stands between them and their ultimate victory – a sleepy rabbit whose ire has been roused.

The battle between Dylan and the four Skeleton warriors is the stuff of future legend. The Skeletons are skilled in the ancient Ninja martial arts. They can strike the right poses; their bony limbs can lash out in chops and kicks to disable or kill an opponent. If the bones that make up those limbs are scattered, they can operate independently of their bodies: arms crawling across the floor and grabbing anything they feel; legs kicking out at anything that passes. But they are facing a rabbit of indomitable spirit, a rabbit who has also been trained in all the martial arts known to man (or, at least, he thinks he has, and that's what counts).

Dylan dispatches the Skeletons in pretty short order, with the help of Ermintrude (who kicks one in the skull with her hoof) and Brian (who bites the ankle of another). Eventually the four Skeletons are nothing but a scattered pile of bones, but the four companions are shocked when the scattered bones begin to slide across the floor and reassemble themselves into something even more terrifying…

Having scattered the Skeletons' bones all over the temple's throne room in a fight to the finish, Dougal, Brian, Dylan and Ermintrude are shocked to discover that the bones can reassemble themselves into one very <u>BIG</u> Skeleton. That hardly seems fair. The giant Skeleton towers over them, its hands grabbing at them, legs propelling it across the flagstones faster than they can run. They were actually better off with the four Ninjas.

The big difference between this Skeleton and the four earlier ones – apart from the fact that it's four times as big – is that it talks. The Ninjas were simply fighting machines, but their big brother has intelligence and memory. The giant Skeleton has been waiting for the arrival of a heroic warrior, prophesied in legend, who will battle it for possession of the magic diamond. And despite the fact that none of the four friends looks particularly heroic (hairy, yes, but heroic would be pushing it), it's not going to be cheated of the battle promised by ancient prophecy.

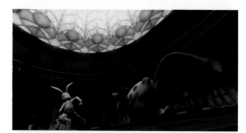

The giant Skeleton stands menacingly between the four friends and the magic diamond that they seek, taunting them about their lack of heroism. Brian, stung by the taunts, loses his temper and charges the Skeleton – very, very slowly. The Skeleton just laughs, and lunges at them, chasing Dougal around the throne that

dominates the centre of the temple, swiping at the dog with its bony fists. Desperately, Dougal dashes onto the throne and pushes some of the buttons that he had discovered earlier – buttons that activate various tricks and traps around the throne room. One in particular causes a stone trapdoor to open beneath the giant Skeleton's feet, and it plummets away into darkness, fingers clutching vainly for Dougal's sandy hair.

The four companions think that's the last they are going to see of the giant Skeleton, but they are wrong. Following a confrontation with Zeebad, they try to find a way out of the temple in their Magic Train, along dark tunnels deep within the temple's interior. Just when they think they're about to make it, from out of the shadows the giant Skeleton grabs at the Train. Looming menacingly, it clutches with bony claws, clambering towards them over the back of the train until …

… it hits its skull against a low beam in the tunnel and smashes itself into four sets of bones again. Heroic Warriors 1, Giant Skeleton 0.

'Man, they don't make crumbling rock causeways like they used to.'
Dylan

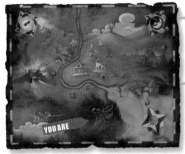

YOU ARE

The Volcano

The Enchanted Land is a land of contrasts. Rolling fields and pastures give way to vast oceans, tropical islands to volcanic crags emerging from pools of sulphurous lava. Everywhere there are signs of a previous civilization: temple carvings, train tracks, tunnels and rocky bridges.

Somewhere far away from the peace and calm of the Enchanted Village, a spire of cracked rock emerges from a pool of lava and claws towards the skies. The sides of the spire, and the surrounding precipices, are sheer and dangerous – just one wrong step could send the unwary traveller plummeting towards a fiery doom.

'Nothing short of a sea of boiling lava
will stop me getting that diamond now!'
Dougal

On top of the spire, protected by a moat of lava, sits a crudely carved rock plinth. On this plinth sits the first of the magic diamonds, kept safe from discovery by the remoteness of its location and the near-impossibility of reaching it. The only way to get from the surrounding precipices to the top of the spire is via a narrow bridge of rock that perilously crosses the lava. Nobody would be so foolhardy as to try … or so you might think.

Zebedee

Before there was an Enchanted Village, before Dougal and Florence and the rest of the friends even existed, there was Zebedee. One of a line of immortal, magical Springers, Zebedee is one of the most powerful beings in all of the Enchanted Land.

For over ten thousand years he has acted as its guardian: appearing whenever he is called, fixing things when they go wrong, gently guiding and befriending the various people and animals and, above all, waiting for a single terrible event to happen while hoping that it never will.

Zebedee is instantly recognizable because he has a spring instead of legs. A coiled length of metal, it enables him to travel rapidly all around the Enchanted Land, bouncing high into the air and arriving as if from nowhere wherever and whenever he is needed. His face is red, his hair is black, his freckles are white and his luxuriant moustache gives him a wise and fatherly air.

Zebedee is a friendly old soul. He hates to tell anyone off, and wants everyone to be happy and content (albeit, within the limits of politeness and consideration for others). Zebedee has seen it all. Whenever Dougal performs a selfish act, or Dylan falls

Zebedee's Favourite Things

Peace and harmony
Bouncing around
Recipes involving spring onions
Winning

Zebedee juggling with the fate of the Enchanted Land

asleep in the middle of something important, Zebedee doesn't get angry; he just tries, in his own calm way, to point out the error of their ways. And when Ermintrude puts on one of her painful concerts, Zebedee seems to enjoy it far more than anyone else.

The other inhabitants of the Enchanted Land don't know much about Zebedee. They are unaware of his immense age and incredible powers, but simply trust that he will always be there to make everything right again with a wave of his hand and a twitch of his moustache. And yet, there are limits to Zebedee's powers, as his friends realize one dark day.

10,000 years ago, Zebedee fought a titanic battle with his ancient counterpart, Zeebad – another wizard Springer – a struggle that plagues his dreams to this day (see Zebedee's Dream). Zebedee eventually won, and imprisoned his dark opponent beneath a magical Roundabout, using three magic diamonds as the means of keeping him from escaping.

And so it remained, while Zebedee watched and waited in case Zeebad escaped.

When Dougal the dog accidentally crashes a stolen tricycle into The Magic Roundabout, disrupting the powerful magic that has kept Zeebad incarcerated for an eternity, Zebedee is fearful of the power that has been unleashed. Quickly, he gathers Dougal, Dylan, Ermintrude and Brian and tells them that they must find the three magic diamonds that he originally used to imprison Zeebad. One of the diamonds is kept on The Magic Roundabout and he must remain behind to guard it. The other two are hidden in remote and dangerous locations, but he gives them two things that will help them on their quest. The first is a map showing the locations of the diamonds. The other is a Magic Box. He also summons the Magic Train to carry them on their quest.

The friends start out on their journey, but danger quickly catches up with them. Dougal is kidnapped by Zeebad, and when the rest of the

Zebedee's Least-favourite Things

Zeebad

Losing, particularly to Zeebad

Recipes involving artichokes

Ermintrude's singing (but he'll never tell)

'Everyone knows that after Winter it's time for SPRING!'
Zebedee

gang rescue him they all find themselves in a face-to-face confrontation with the wicked Springer. About to be destroyed, they call for Zebedee. The kindly magician abandons his post at The Magic Roundabout and *boings* to their aid. Alas, while saving them from certain death at Zeebad's hands (or, rather, moustache), Zebedee is struck by his cruel counterpart's beams of enchanted energy. Frozen to the edge of a cliff, Zebedee can only struggle in vain as Zeebad uses his powers to cut away the cliff edge and send him plummeting toward his doom!

With their mentor apparently dead, Dougal, Dylan, Ermintrude and Brian are on the verge of giving up. What's the point of going on? they wonder. Even if they find the magic diamonds, surely they need Zebedee's powers to use them. In the end, they keep on going in the hope that all is not lost. After all, it's the right thing to do, and if Zebedee has taught them anything it's that they should always strive to do the right thing.

Fortunately for the Enchanted Land, Zebedee did not die. Encased in ice, he survived his long fall and, when his friends finally defeat Zeebad and banish him again, Zebedee is freed. Returning to The Magic Roundabout he uses his immense powers to set everything right again. First he repairs Soldier Sam – within whose chest the third magical diamond had been hidden – and returns him to his position on top of the Roundabout. Next he thanks the blue Moose for his bravery and returns it to its natural colour. Finally he uses his magic to create a celebration for everyone.

The Enchanted Land is safe once more, and Zebedee is in charge.

Until the next time Zeebad escapes…

'Everything's worked out – in a Roundabout kind of way.'
Zebedee

Zebedee's Dream

*Even now, 10,000 years after their epic battle,
Zebedee still has dreams about his
ancient nemesis Zeebad.*

The dream always starts off at night, with a bright moon illuminating a dark and rocky landscape. Suddenly, out of nowhere, a blast of energy shoots past Zebedee and smashes into the ground just in front of him, exploding in a puff of smoke. Zebedee reacts quickly and takes immediate evasive action, jumping left and right to escape the energy blasts that are coming thick and fast.

Pursued relentlessly by his unseen attacker, Zebedee bounds into the darkness. About to take a last spring forward, he pulls up short just in time to avoid plummeting into a gaping abyss and going over a glacial precipice in the shape of an enormous head. There is something ominously familiar about this face carved into the ice. Something disturbing.

As the shooting intensifies, Zebedee skillfully manages to spring from one crevice to another, just managing to keep his balance but, just as he leaps across a gap, an energy blast catches his spring and sends him flying to the edge of an overhang. He just manages to cling onto the edge with one hand, but no sooner has he found a hold, when another blast sweeps him off.

Zebedee tumbles helplessly but, miraculously catches hold of the last ledge and dangles helplessly above the abyss. As he looks up, a large, malevolent shadow creeps across him.

Zebedee stares straight into the leering face of his now arch-enemy, Zeebad.

No longer able to hold on, Zebedee plunges into the depths below, and wakes screaming from his nightmare, fear still registering in his eyes. He sits bolt upright, moustache twitching and adrenaline pumping and

**Zeebad holds the
fate of the
Enchanted Land
in the palm(s) of
his hand(s).**

looks around as a bead of sweat drips off his brow. Realizing he's safe, he springs out of bed to check that everything in the Enchanted Village is fine. Everything looks peaceful and quiet. For now. But the dream will come again, and one day Zebedee fears it will no longer be just a dream. One day Zeebad will return…

Zeebad

A nasty sorcerer with a blue face, a spring instead of legs and no redeeming social graces, Zeebad has been thought of as nothing more than a myth.

With his deep voice, his black hair plaited back into a rather stylish pigtail and his moustache curling luxuriously, Zeebad is one of a race of ancient and powerful Springers who once inhabited the Enchanted Land. Now, all that's left of that race are ancient temples and ruined statues – and the last two magicians left bouncing – Zeebad and Zebedee.

Zeebad can be thought of as the dark side of his ancient adversary, Zebedee. Where Zebedee is kind, Zeebad is cruel. Where Zebedee is uncomplaining, Zeebad is impatient. Where Zebedee is tolerant, Zeebad has no time for anyone apart from himself. And, most importantly, where Zebedee is good, Zeebad is unredeemably evil. He has no good side to appeal to, no inner warmth.

The only similarities between Zebedee and Zeebad are their immense powers, which are evenly matched – and their intelligence. The trouble is that 10,000 years of imprisonment has concentrated Zeebad's intelligence into a single thought – a dark scheme of revenge.

That day, all those years ago, was the last time Zeebad and Zebedee saw each other. Zeebad was condemned to spend the rest of eternity in a place nobody would ever find him and from where he could never escape – a volcanic cavern deep beneath the Earth.

But one day, everything changed…

'And so, it ends. My nemesis, finally vanquished forever. It's almost enough to make one weep, if only I wasn't so very, very happy.'
Zeebad

'Today,
one
soldier,
tomorrow
the world!'
Zeebad

Dougal loses control of the Candy Seller's tricycle and has a terrible accident. It crashes into the Roundabout. The damage caused is enough to disrupt the protective spells that Zebedee had placed on the Roundabout, and Zeebad in the midst of the chaos, shoots through the canopy of the Roundabout away from the Enchanted Village, ending up far away and safe – for the moment.

Zeebad's thirst for power has been undimmed by his millennia-long incarceration, and he has a burning desire to wipe the Enchanted Land clean of the grass, flowers and wildlife that have infested it. He decides to make everything icy and cold – but for that he will need to obtain the magic diamonds. He will also need to defeat Zebedee, and that might take some doing. And although his powers are slightly dimmed by the passing of many centuries, Zeebad quickly realises that his chances will be increased if he recruits help, for Zebedee will undoubtedly be assisted by his own friends. Zeebad uses his magical powers to enlarge a wooden soldier to a useful size. He proves to be an ideal sidekick, since he is trained to obey orders without question.

On the way back to his old lair, Zeebad comes across Dougal, the sandy-haired dog who accidentally freed Zeebad in the first place and is now part of the team of unlikely companions who are attempting to locate the three magic diamonds before Zeebad does.

'When I leave someone for dead, I expect them to die! Can't you even do that right?'
Zeebad

Zeebad imprisons Dougal in an ice cage and orders Soldier Sam to torture the dog in an attempt to extract information from him. Dougal's friends attempt to rescue him – Ermintrude is lowered through a hole in the cavern's ceiling – but as they make their getaway an enraged Zeebad springs up and grabs hold of Ermintrude's tail, pulling her back inside the cave. To his fury, Brian (attached to a length of rope) plunges through the roof of the cave towards Zeebad and has the temerity to bite his wrist! Things have changed a lot since Zeebad was last at large. People used to respect him! He watches the four heroes leave, but is soon in hot pursuit to get the map showing the location of the diamonds that Dougal accidentally mentioned.

Outside the cavern, on a field of ice near to the edge of a glacial cliff, Zeebad confronts the four companions. He wants the map – and he wants to get them out of the way – but they call on Zebedee for help. In moments, Zebedee is by their side, and once more faces down his old opponent. The two of them fly at one another, their springs entangling. Blows are exchanged, bolts of magical energy flung back and forth. And then, at a crucial moment, Zebedee's attention is distracted when he spies Soldier Sam menacing his friends. Before he can act, Zeebad takes advantage of his distraction to blast him with an energy bolt. Helpless in the snow, Zebedee is stunned as Zeebad uses his magical powers to freeze his spring to the ground, and then sends the edge of the glacier and Zebedee plunging away into darkness. At last he has rid himself of his age-old adversary!

The four heroes escape on their Magical Train, but Zeebad follows them since he knows they have the map. He and Soldier Sam track them to a volcanic crag surrounded by a moat of lava where, many years ago, Zebedee hid the first of the diamonds. And when the four heroes locate the diamond, Zeebad pounces, taking the diamond and the map away from them and destroying the only way they can get off the crag, thus sealing their doom.

Zeebad and Soldier Sam set off across a vast ocean in search of the second magic diamond, and eventually make landfall on a tropical island far away that houses the ruins of an ancient temple. When Zeebad is menaced by a carnivorous plant and Soldier Sam almost falls victim to a booby-trap, the wicked enchanter decides to let discretion be the better part of valour. He needs someone else to get inside, risk all the dangers and retrieve the second diamond for him, and when the four adventurers arrive on the island in a balloon, having escaped from the volcanic peak he had left them on, he knows just who to choose.

True to form, the heroes retrieve the diamond, and Zeebad takes it away from them at their moment of greatest triumph. But he still doesn't know where the final diamond is – the map is remarkably unclear on that point – and so he gives chase on a Mole Train that he has discovered deep in the bowels of the temple. During the chase he discovers, from a confused Brian, the information that the diamond is actually back on The Magic Roundabout, and so he makes for the Enchanted Village, abandoning the four heroes and Soldier Sam in the process.

Back at the now-frozen Enchanted Village, Zeebad is frustrated that he cannot find the third and final diamond that he needs to turn the world cold. His rage is about to erupt when Soldier Sam turns up, having had a change of heart. He challenges Zeebad to abandon his plans, but the wicked enchanter responds by directing a magical energy blast directly at Soldier Sam's chest. The brave soldier falls to the ground, mortally wounded (well, as mortally wounded as a wooden soldier can be), and Zeebad is astounded to discover the third diamond hidden within Soldier Sam's chest.

'Sorry we can't stay, but you know how it is – people to rule, places to freeze.'
Zeebad

Now in possession of all the magical diamonds, Zeebad summons all his powers to bear. Refracted through the diamonds, his energy blasts are now powerful enough to freeze the sun itself – but he is interrupted by the arrival of four tired and cold heroes. In a dramatic and energetic encounter, they try to take the diamonds away from him, and Zeebad tries to use his powers to retain them. Eventually the friends succeed and the three diamonds are placed back in their rightful place on top of The Magic Roundabout, and a glowing vortex sucks up all the ice and snow. Recoiling in fear, Zeebad tries to escape but the vortex grabs him.

And so Zeebad ends up back where he started – imprisoned in a volcanic hellhole somewhere deep beneath The Magic Roundabout, about as far from his beloved ice and snow as it's possible to get.

'Now, you dim-witted draft excluder, tell me everything.'
Zeebad

Zeebad's Alternative Moustaches

The Walrus   *The Poirot*   *The Dali*   *The Chaplin*

Zeebad's Lair

All villains need a lair. A place where they can relax and dream up schemes for ruling the world and oppressing the masses. A sanctum decorated in lavish style that reflects and magnifies their glory and makes them feel comfortable and secure. A place where heroes are automatically at a disadvantage, and can be easily imprisoned and taunted.

When Zeebad first tried to freeze the sun, he created for himself a lair that suited his taste in décor: a cold, frozen cave of ice-encrusted rock, spartan but with a certain stark appeal. Sadly, he never got to enjoy it very much thanks to that killjoy magician Zebedee who imprisoned him in a volcanic cavern beneath The Magic Roundabout.

Opposite: Zeebad's attempts to tail Brian may have been spotted. Left: Ermintrude, left in a state of suspended animation.

'To my old lair! We shall plan our line of attack.'
Zeebad

'Free at last!
It took ten
thousand
years, but the
best things
are worth
waiting for.
Power.
Revenge.
Power.'
Zeebad

On his escape, Zeebad quickly decides that he needs his base of operations once more, a place from where he can set out to obtain the three magic diamonds he needs.

Everything in Zeebad's lair is made of ice – chairs, tables, statues, even the crockery. One of the features that the fiendish magician is proudest of is the ice box – a box whose walls are made of frozen water. And he finds an immediate use for it, putting Dougal the dog inside. There's also a large mirror in which Zeebad spends inordinate amounts of time admiring himself, preening and stroking his moustache. Unfortunately the cave also contains a hole in the ceiling just large enough for a cow to be lowered through on a rope in order to rescue an unfortunate dog. Perhaps Zeebad should have forseen that eventuality when he first created his lair.

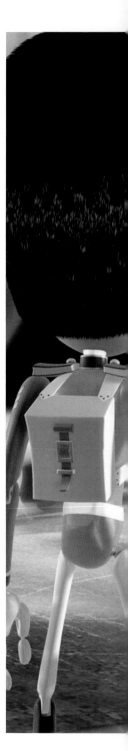

Zeebad's Prison

Deep beneath the flowers and grass of the Enchanted Village, beneath the hopping bunnies and happily playing children, lies another world. A strange, dark, disturbing world.

A world of lava and shimmering heat, of twisted stalactites and stalagmites clawing out of the rock walls of a volcanic cavern. It's the place where the nasty warlock Zeebad has been imprisoned for the past 10,000 years, and will probably be imprisoned in for the next 10,000 as well.

And it's not meant to be comfortable.

Zeebad's prison has been deliberately designed to be deeply unpleasant. Zeebad loves the cold, so the cavern is as hot as possible. Zeebad loves to bounce, so the rock roof is low. And Zeebad loves to impose his will on anyone else who is around, so the cavern is completely uninhabited. The magic of The Magic Roundabout, far far above, also prevents Zeebad

Zeebad proudly demonstrates his new icebox to Soldier Sam.

from using his own powers to freeze anything. There is nothing for him to do apart from plan his vengeance in meticulous detail – so there is no hope that Zebedee will know what's coming next.

Following his brief escape from captivity, when Zeebad's fiendish plan to freeze the sun is defeated by four plucky adventurers and the Magic Train, Zeebad is sucked into a magical vortex and deposited back in the prison from whence he had escaped not long before. Momentarily comforted by the ice and snow that was sucked into the vortex with him – the last remnants of his plan to freeze the Enchanted Land – he watches with fury as it all melts

'Curses, imprisoned once more.'
Zeebad

146

away in the fierce heat of the molten rock, leaving him stranded again in the worst possible environment.

And, far, far above Zeebad's head, The Magic Roundabout turns merrily on, while children climb on board and call happily to one another, entirely unaware that it's the magic of The Magic Roundabout that will keep Zeebad in his fiery prison for all eternity.

And yet, he is still alive. And still planning for his next escape…

ZZZZZZ…

At the end of their journey across the Enchanted Land,
Dougal and his friends are exhausted.

They've had a trying couple of days, what with the world being turned to snow and ice, travelling along rickety rock ledges in a Magic Train, battling millennia-old skeletons and otherwise putting pay to the plans of a blue-skinned maniac with dreams of frozen glory. After catching up with their friends who have now been released, and are warming up nicely, and a few spins on the newly restored Magic Roundabout, there's only one thing left to do.

With a twirl of his moustache, and a seraphic smile upon his Springer face, Zebedee announces the words the whole of the Enchanted Village's inhabitants have been waiting for…

'Time for bed!'